MATT

FRANCES MACKAY

The fourth book in the series
ON THE BALL

Ben and Matt were in the school football team.

Football, football, football.

All they could think about was football.

Every day, Ben and Matt tried hard to get better at football.

They ran to school every morning to keep fit.

They practised passing.

They practised goal shooting.

They practised dribbling.

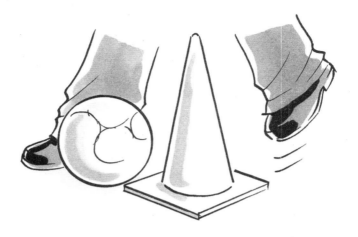

They practised being part of a team.

And after school they ran all the way home.

They played with their friends in the park.

They watched their heroes on TV.

They read about football.

They talked about football.

There was nothing else but football.

Being in the team was great — but they still didn't have a football strip.

One week, at football practice, Mr Jones arrived with a police officer.

'This is PC Hunter,' Mr Jones said. 'He wants to talk to you all about the stolen kit.'

'We think we know who stole your strip,' said PC Hunter.

Everyone's faces lit up.

'Trouble is, they're hiding it somewhere and we haven't found out where yet. But we will,' he said.

'Well, that *is* good news,' said Mr Jones.

'If any of you see anything, let me know. But don't try to do anything yourselves. Just contact me at the station, OK?' said PC Hunter.

Everyone went home full of hope that the kit would be found.

'We need to look for our strip,' said Ben. 'I bet we could find it.'

'Shouldn't we leave it up to the police?' asked Matt.

'You heard PC Hunter. He said to keep a look out,' said Ben.

'Yeah, but he also said to leave it up to them,' said Matt.

'It won't hurt to look,' said Ben.

Later that week, Matt met Ben at the old shoe factory.

'What are we doing here?' asked Matt.

'It's perfect,' said Ben.

'Perfect for what?' asked Matt.

'A perfect place to hide our stolen strip,' said Ben. 'I've been thinking about this place all week.'

'You're right,' said Matt. 'Let's have a poke around.'

Ben and Matt spent two hours looking around the old factory.

They found nothing.

Just as they were leaving, Ben saw something.

Poking out of a cupboard in the office was something bright red.

'Hang on a minute, Matt. Let's have a look at this,' he said.

Stuffed inside the cupboard was their school strip!

'Yes! Detective Ben wins the day,' yelled Ben, as he jumped around the room.

Matt pulled a shirt out. It was torn to shreds.

'Look at this!' said Matt.

Ben stopped jumping about.

They pulled out more shirts.

They were all ripped to bits.

'Why would anyone do this?' asked Ben.

They ran to get PC Hunter. He came back to the factory with them.

He was happy they'd found the strip, but he wasn't happy about them going into the old factory.

'It's dangerous here, you could have been hurt,' he said. 'Now promise me you'll leave it up to us from now on, OK?'

Ben and Matt walked home together.

'I hope they find out who did it,' said Matt.

'Yeah, but we still don't have a kit,' said Ben.

There was more bad news to come.

The next morning, Ben went to Matt's house as usual.

Matt's mum opened the door.

'Oh, hello Ben. I'm afraid Matt can't come to school today,' she said.

'Is he sick?' asked Ben.

'No, no. He's ... um ... well, you see, Matt's going to a different school from now on,' she said.

Ben looked puzzled.

'But why? What's happened?' he asked.

'Sorry Ben, but I can't say at the moment. Perhaps it might be best if you don't call any more,' said Matt's mum, as she closed the door.

Ben stood very still, facing the closed door.

He felt cold and numb.

What was going on? Matt hadn't said a word to him about this all week.

Ben couldn't believe it.

His very best friend was going away to a different school and didn't want to see him any more.

What about the team?

Matt was one of the best players.

What would they do without him?

Slowly Ben walked to school, feeling sad and upset.

He couldn't believe what Matt's mum had said.

What was going on?

The day dragged at school.

Ben didn't want to practise football without Matt.

He didn't want to do anything.

He wasn't even thinking about the torn kit they'd found any more.

When he got home that afternoon, his mum was in the kitchen.

'Hello, love. Any more news about the torn kit?' she asked.

'Umm ... no,' said Ben. 'Mum, did you know about Matt? Did you know he was going away?'

'Well ... I ... ' she replied.

'You did, didn't you? What's going on? Why isn't anyone telling me anything?' yelled Ben.

'Ben, I'm sorry, but Matt's mother told me not to say anything. She wanted you two to have some fun together before he went,' she said.

'But why's he going away?' asked Ben.

'I think you'd better ask him that,' she said.

'I can't. Matt's mum said not to call round any more,' said Ben.

'Yes, I know. But Matt rang me to say he's waiting for you at the park. Go and see him yourself, Ben,' she said.

Ben ran all the way to the park.

He was so upset he was almost crying.

When he got there, he could see Matt sitting on one of the swings.

Matt waved to Ben and called him over.

'Hi Ben,' said Matt. 'I'm glad you came.'

'What's going on, Matt?' asked Ben crossly.

'It's my dad. He's lost his job and we have to move away,' said Matt.

'Why didn't you tell me?' asked Ben. 'Lots of people lose their jobs. It doesn't mean we have to stop seeing each other.'

'Dad lost his job six months ago — and didn't tell us. Now our house is being repossessed and Mum is really upset. I only found out myself today,' said Matt.

'Oh,' said Ben.

He didn't know what else to say.

'We have to rent a house now. I've already been to see my new school. I start there next week,' said Matt.

'Can't you travel back to see me and go to football practice, so you can still be on the team?'

'It's too far,' said Matt.

'Oh,' said Ben again.

'I've got to go now,' said Matt.

Ben stood watching as Matt walked away.

He felt as if he would never see his friend again.

Suddenly, being on the football team didn't seem so important.

What was he going to do without Matt?

That night, Ben lay awake, thinking.

He thought and he thought, until he had a plan.

Next morning, Ben spoke to his mum.

'Mum, I've been thinking about Matt and how much I'm going to miss him. The football team will miss him too, because he's our best player,' said Ben.

'Yes I know, Ben. It's all very sad, but what can we do?' she asked.

'Can Matt come and live with us for the rest of the school year?' asked Ben.

'What?' said Mum. 'There's already four of us here. Even if his parents did agree, where would he sleep?'

'In my room – it's big enough. Oh, please, Mum, please say you'll think about it. At least this way we can still be friends and still play on the team,' said Ben.

'I'll think about it,' said Mum. 'Now, off to school or you'll be late!'

At the next football practice, Mr Jones told them that his idea for getting a new football strip hadn't worked out as planned.

'I'm sorry team, but you'll have to play in your PE kits for the first match,' he said.

It was too much for Ben.

Not only was he losing his best friend and team-mate, but now they had to play without a proper football strip.

How could they ever be a winning team now?

The next book in the series is:

FIRST MATCH

HOW MANY HAVE YOU READ?